Packages and Groups

MULTIPLICATION AND DIVISION

TERC

Investigations in Number, Data, and Space®

Dale Seymour Publications®

Menlo Park, California

The *Investigations* curriculum was developed at TERC (formerly Technical Education Research Centers) in collaboration with Kent State University and the State University of New York at Buffalo. The work was supported in part by National Science Foundation Grant No. ESI-9050210. TERC is a nonprofit company working to improve mathematics and science education. TERC is located at 2067 Massachusetts Avenue, Cambridge, MA 02140.

This project was supported, in part, by the
National Science Foundation
Opinions expressed are those of the authors and not necessarily those of the Foundation

Managing Editor: Catherine Anderson
Series Editor: Beverly Cory
Manuscript Editor: Karen Becker
ESL Consultant: Nancy Sokol Green
Production/Manufacturing Director: Janet Yearian
Production/Manufacturing Coordinator: Joe Conte
Design Manager: Jeff Kelly
Design: Don Taka
Illustrations: Barbara Epstein-Eagle, Hollis Burkhart
Composition: Archetype Book Composition

This book is published by Dale Seymour Publications®, an imprint of Addison Wesley Longman, Inc.

Dale Seymour Publications
2725 Sand Hill Road
Menlo Park, CA 94025
Customer Service: 800-872-1100

[redacted]

DALE SEYMOUR PUBLICATIONS®

Order number DS47009
ISBN 1-57232-762-6
1 2 3 4 5 6 7 8 9 10-ML-01 00 99 98 97

Printed on Recycled Paper

Contents

*Repeated-use sheet

*Repeated-use sheet

Name ______________________________ Date

Student Sheet 1

Making a Multiplication Table

	1	2	3	4	5	6	7	8	9	10	11	12
1	•											
2												
3												
4												
5												
6												
7												
8												
9												
10												
11												
12												

Name ______________________________ Date

Student Sheet 1

Making a Multiplication Table

	1	2	3	4	5	6	7	8	9	10	11	12
1	•											
2												
3												
4												
5												
6												
7												
8												
9												
10												
11												
12												

To the Family

Making a Multiplication Table

Sessions 1–2

Math Content
Becoming familiar with multiplication pairs

Materials
Student Sheet 1
Pencil
Array Cards (optional)

In class, we have been using arrays (a rectangular arrangement of objects in rows and columns) to investigate multiplication. Students used the Array Cards to complete multiplication tables and looked for patterns in the table. For homework, your child will complete a second multiplication table (without looking at the multiplication table made in class), using the patterns students noticed when making the first table in school. Your child may use Array Cards if needed. You should have a set at home from the earlier unit *Arrays and Shares*.

	1	2	3	4	5	6	7	8	9	10	11	12
1	1	2	3	4	5	6	7	8	9	10	11	12
2	2	4	6	8	10	12	14	16	18	20	22	24
3	3	6	9	12	15	18	21	24	27	30	33	36
4	4	8	12	16	20	24	28	32	36	40	44	48
5	5	10	15	20	25	30	35	40	45	50	55	60
6	6	12	18	24	30	36	42	48	54	60	66	72
7	7	14	21	28	35	42	49	56	63	70	77	84
8	8	16	24	32	40	48	56	64	72	80	88	96
9	9	18	27	36	45	54	63	72	81	90	99	108
10	10	20	30	40	50	60	70	80	90	100	110	120
11	11	22	33	44	55	66	77	88	99	110	121	132
12	12	24	36	48	60	72	84	96	108	120	132	144

COMPLETED MULTIPLICATION TABLE

	1	2	3	4	5	6	7	8	9	10	11	12
1	1	2	3	4	5	6	7	8	9	10	11	12
2	2	4	6	8	10	12	14	16	18	20	22	24
3	3	6	9	12	15	18	21	24	27	30	33	36
4	4	8	12	16	20	24	28	32	36	40	44	48
5	5	10	15	20	25	30	35	40	45	50	55	60
6	6	12	18	24	30	36	42	48	54	60	66	72
7	7	14	21	28	35	42	49	56	63	70	77	84
8	8	16	24	32	40	48	56	64	72	80	88	96
9	9	18	27	36	45	54	63	72	81	90	99	108
10	10	20	30	40	50	60	70	80	90	100	110	120
11	11	22	33	44	55	66	77	88	99	110	121	132
12	12	24	36	48	60	72	84	96	108	120	132	144

COMPLETED MULTIPLICATION TABLE

	1	2	3	4	5	6	7	8	9	10	11	12
1	1	2	3	4	5	6	7	8	9	10	11	12
2	2	4	6	8	10	12	14	16	18	20	22	24
3	3	6	9	12	15	18	21	24	27	30	33	36
4	4	8	12	16	20	24	28	32	36	40	44	48
5	5	10	15	20	25	30	35	40	45	50	55	60
6	6	12	18	24	30	36	42	48	54	60	66	72
7	7	14	21	28	35	42	49	56	63	70	77	84
8	8	16	24	32	40	48	56	64	72	80	88	96
9	9	18	27	36	45	54	63	72	81	90	99	108
10	10	20	30	40	50	60	70	80	90	100	110	120
11	11	22	33	44	55	66	77	88	99	110	121	132
12	12	24	36	48	60	72	84	96	108	120	132	144

COMPLETED MULTIPLICATION TABLE

	1	2	3	4	5	6	7	8	9	10	11	12
1	1	2	3	4	5	6	7	8	9	10	11	12
2	2	4	6	8	10	12	14	16	18	20	22	24
3	3	6	9	12	15	18	21	24	27	30	33	36
4	4	8	12	16	20	24	28	32	36	40	44	48
5	5	10	15	20	25	30	35	40	45	50	55	60
6	6	12	18	24	30	36	42	48	54	60	66	72
7	7	14	21	28	35	42	49	56	63	70	77	84
8	8	16	24	32	40	48	56	64	72	80	88	96
9	9	18	27	36	45	54	63	72	81	90	99	108
10	10	20	30	40	50	60	70	80	90	100	110	120
11	11	22	33	44	55	66	77	88	99	110	121	132
12	12	24	36	48	60	72	84	96	108	120	132	144

Name ______________________________ Date

Student Sheet 1

Making a Multiplication Table

	1	2	3	4	5	6	7	8	9	10	11	12
1	•											
2												
3												
4												
5												
6												
7												
8												
9												
10												
11												
12												

1	2	3	4	5	6	7	8	9	10
11	12	13	14	15	16	17	18	19	20
21	22	23	24	25	26	27	28	29	30
31	32	33	34	35	36	37	38	39	40
41	42	43	44	45	46	47	48	49	50
51	52	53	54	55	56	57	58	59	60
61	62	63	64	65	66	67	68	69	70
71	72	73	74	75	76	77	78	79	80
81	82	83	84	85	86	87	88	89	90
91	92	93	94	95	96	97	98	99	100
101	102	103	104	105	106	107	108	109	110
111	112	113	114	115	116	117	118	119	120
121	122	123	124	125	126	127	128	129	130
131	132	133	134	135	136	137	138	139	140
141	142	143	144	145	146	147	148	149	150
151	152	153	154	155	156	157	158	159	160
161	162	163	164	165	166	167	168	169	170
171	172	173	174	175	176	177	178	179	180
181	182	183	184	185	186	187	188	189	190
191	192	193	194	195	196	197	198	199	200
201	202	203	204	205	206	207	208	209	210
211	212	213	214	215	216	217	218	219	220
221	222	223	224	225	226	227	228	229	230
231	232	233	234	235	236	237	238	239	240
241	242	243	244	245	246	247	248	249	250
251	252	253	254	255	256	257	258	259	260
261	262	263	264	265	266	267	268	269	270
271	272	273	274	275	276	277	278	279	280
281	282	283	284	285	286	287	288	289	290
291	292	293	294	295	296	297	298	299	300

To the Student: Your teacher may ask you to save this chart for use in other activities.

1	2	3	4	5	6	7	8	9	10
11	12	13	14	15	16	17	18	19	20
21	22	23	24	25	26	27	28	29	30
31	32	33	34	35	36	37	38	39	40
41	42	43	44	45	46	47	48	49	50
51	52	53	54	55	56	57	58	59	60
61	62	63	64	65	66	67	68	69	70
71	72	73	74	75	76	77	78	79	80
81	82	83	84	85	86	87	88	89	90
91	92	93	94	95	96	97	98	99	100
101	102	103	104	105	106	107	108	109	110
111	112	113	114	115	116	117	118	119	120
121	122	123	124	125	126	127	128	129	130
131	132	133	134	135	136	137	138	139	140
141	142	143	144	145	146	147	148	149	150
151	152	153	154	155	156	157	158	159	160
161	162	163	164	165	166	167	168	169	170
171	172	173	174	175	176	177	178	179	180
181	182	183	184	185	186	187	188	189	190
191	192	193	194	195	196	197	198	199	200
201	202	203	204	205	206	207	208	209	210
211	212	213	214	215	216	217	218	219	220
221	222	223	224	225	226	227	228	229	230
231	232	233	234	235	236	237	238	239	240
241	242	243	244	245	246	247	248	249	250
251	252	253	254	255	256	257	258	259	260
261	262	263	264	265	266	267	268	269	270
271	272	273	274	275	276	277	278	279	280
281	282	283	284	285	286	287	288	289	290
291	292	293	294	295	296	297	298	299	300

To the Student: Your teacher may ask you to save this chart for use in other activities.

Name Date

Student Sheet 2

Making Multiple Towers

Choose any two of the following numbers to skip count by. List and record the multiples for each number.

15, 18, 20, 24, 32, 36, 40, 45, 55, 60, 64, 70, 72, 75

My first number is ________________.

List of multiples:

My second number is ________________.

List of multiples:

To the Family

Making Multiple Towers

Sessions 4–5

Math Content
Finding multiples of larger numbers

Materials
Student Sheet 2
300 chart

In class, we have been building Multiple Towers. We choose a number to count by (for example, 50) and then write each number (50, 100, 150, and so on) on a stick-on note or index card and attach it to the wall, starting at the floor and going as high as the teacher is tall.

For homework, your child will choose two numbers from the list on Student Sheet 2 and make a list of the multiples for that numbers. Your child may use a 300 chart as a tool to begin the list. You might remind your child to take this sheet to school so we can use it to build more multiple towers.

300 CHART

1	2	3	4	5	6	7	8	9	10
11	12	13	14	15	16	17	18	19	20
21	22	23	24	25	26	27	28	29	30
31	32	33	34	35	36	37	38	39	40
41	42	43	44	45	46	47	48	49	50
51	52	53	54	55	56	57	58	59	60
61	62	63	64	65	66	67	68	69	70
71	72	73	74	75	76	77	78	79	80
81	82	83	84	85	86	87	88	89	90
91	92	93	94	95	96	97	98	99	100
101	102	103	104	105	106	107	108	109	110
111	112	113	114	115	116	117	118	119	120
121	122	123	124	125	126	127	128	129	130
131	132	133	134	135	136	137	138	139	140
141	142	143	144	145	146	147	148	149	150
151	152	153	154	155	156	157	158	159	160
161	162	163	164	165	166	167	168	169	170
171	172	173	174	175	176	177	178	179	180
181	182	183	184	185	186	187	188	189	190
191	192	193	194	195	196	197	198	199	200
201	202	203	204	205	206	207	208	209	210
211	212	213	214	215	216	217	218	219	220
221	222	223	224	225	226	227	228	229	230
231	232	233	234	235	236	237	238	239	240
241	242	243	244	245	246	247	248	249	250
251	252	253	254	255	256	257	258	259	260
261	262	263	264	265	266	267	268	269	270
271	272	273	274	275	276	277	278	279	280
281	282	283	284	285	286	287	288	289	290
291	292	293	294	295	296	297	298	299	300

To the Student: Your teacher may ask you to save this chart for use in other activities.

To the Family

Making Multiple Towers

Sessions 4–5

Math Content
Finding multiples of larger numbers

Materials
Student Sheet 2
300 chart

In class, we have been building Multiple Towers. We choose a number to count by (for example, 50) and then write each number (50, 100, 150, and so on) on a stick-on note or index card and attach it to the wall, starting at the floor and going as high as the teacher is tall.

For homework, your child will choose two numbers from the list on Student Sheet 2 and make a list of the multiples for that number. Your child may use a 300 chart as a tool to begin the list. You might remind your child to take this sheet to school so we can use it to build more multiple towers.

Name Date

Student Sheet 3

A Cluster of Problems

First, make an estimate for 34×9.

Estimate: ________________

Now, make up a cluster of problems to help you solve 34×9. Solve each of the problems. Show your work and write about how each helped you solve 34×9.

To the Family

A Cluster of Problems

Session 1

Math Content

Breaking larger numbers into more-manageable pieces to multiply them more easily

Materials

Student Sheet 3
Pencil

In class, we have been using Cluster Problems, a group of related problems, to solve harder multiplication problems. For example, to solve 42×8, you might use several of the following problems:

2×8

4×8

10×8

40×8

42×8

For homework, your child will make up a cluster of problems to help solve the problem 34×9 and write about how each of the problems helped him or her find the solution.

Name Date

Student Sheet 4

32 × 21

Solve this multiplication problem in two ways:

$32 \times 21 =$

Write about how you solved this problem.
Be sure to include:

- what materials you used to solve this problem
- how you solved it
- an explanation of your thinking as you solved it

First Way

Second Way

Name Date

Cluster Problems (page 1 of 2)

Make an estimate for the last problem in each cluster.
Then solve the problems in the clusters.

6×20

3×20

30×20

$\mathbf{36 \times 20}$

Estimate for 36×20 ____________

6×3

20×3

26×3

$\mathbf{26 \times 30}$

Estimate for 26×30 ____________

Checking Your Estimates (page 1 of 2)

Make an estimate for the first problem in each cluster. Then solve the problems in the clusters.

[illegible] × [illegible]

2 × 20

29 × 20

Estimate for 29 × 20: ______

20 × 3

[illegible]

20 × 30

Estimate for [illegible]: ______

Name Date

Student Sheet 5

Cluster Problems (page 2 of 2)

30×3

40×5

40×30

43×35

Estimate for 43×35 ____________

10×15

9×15

20×15

29×15

Estimate for 29×15 ____________

Name Date

Student Sheet 6

Making Cluster Problems (page 1 of 2)

Make up a cluster of problems to help you solve each multiplication problem. Exchange cluster problems with a partner and solve each other's clusters.

$39 \times 15 =$ Estimate ____________

$44 \times 28 =$ Estimate ____________

Name Date

Student Sheet 6

Making Cluster Problems (page 2 of 2)

Make up a cluster of problems to help you solve each multiplication problem. Exchange cluster problems with a partner and solve each other's clusters.

$64 \times 31 =$ Estimate ___________

$59 \times 29 =$ Estimate ___________

Name ____________________ Date ____________

Student Sheet 7

Cluster Problems

Make an estimate for the last problem in each cluster.
Then solve the problems in the clusters.

3×25

10×25

20×25

$\mathbf{23 \times 25}$

Estimate for 23×25 ____________

9×30

10×32

20×32

$\mathbf{19 \times 32}$

Estimate for 19×32 ____________

To the Family

More Cluster Problems

Sessions 2–3

Math Content

Breaking numbers into more-familiar parts
Using landmark numbers to make estimates

Materials

Student Sheet 7
Pencil

In class, we have continued to estimate and solve double-digit multiplication problems. For homework, your child will make an estimate for the last problem in each cluster on Student Sheet 7 and then solve the problems. Remind your child to return this homework to school so that students can exchange their cluster problem solutions with each other.

Name ______________________________ Date ______________

Student Sheet 8

Other People's Strategies

Ask at least two family members, older siblings, or neighbors to solve one or more of the following problems mentally.

23×9 5×32 21×14

With the help of each adult, record the strategy he or she used so that you can explain it to someone else. Remember to take this sheet back to class.

The problem we worked on is ________________.

This was the strategy we used to solve this problem:

The problem we worked on is ________________.

This was the strategy we used to solve this problem:

To the Family

Other People's Strategies

Sessions 2–3

Math Content
Explaining and comparing strategies for solving multiplication problems

Materials
Student Sheet 8
Pencil

To practice explaining and comparing strategies for solving multiplication problems, your child will interview at least two adults, older siblings, or neighbors about the strategies they use to multiply mentally. With the help of the adult, your child will write down the strategy so that it can be explained to someone else. Remind your child to take this homework to school so that we can record some of the strategies on a poster.

Name Date

Student Sheet 9

Pencils

Pencils come in packages of 12.

1. How many packages of pencils do you have to open to give 2 pencils to everyone in our class?

2. How many packages do you have to open to give 4 pencils to everyone in our class?

3. How many packages do you have to open to give 6 pencils to everyone in our class?

Name Date

Student Sheet 10

More Pencil Problems

Solve the following problems. You may use counting materials or calculators, if available. Show how you solved each problem.

1. Pencils come in packages of 12. How many packages would you have to open to give 1 pencil to everyone in our school?

2. How many would you have to open to give everyone in our school 2 pencils each?

3. If pencils came in packages of 18, how many packages would you have to open to give everyone in our class 2 pencils?

To the Family

More Pencil Problems

Sessions 1–2

Math Content

Recognizing and interpreting division situations
Solving division problems

Materials

Student Sheet 10
Pencil
Counting materials or calculators (optional)

In class, we have been using real-life problems about classroom supplies to represent different types of division situations. To continue this work, your child will solve the problems on Student Sheet 10. Your child may want to use materials to count or calculators, if available.

1	2	3	4	5	6	7	8	9	10
11	12	13	14	15	16	17	18	19	20
21	22	23	24	25	26	27	28	29	30
31	32	33	34	35	36	37	38	39	40
41	42	43	44	45	46	47	48	49	50
51	52	53	54	55	56	57	58	59	60
61	62	63	64	65	66	67	68	69	70
71	72	73	74	75	76	77	78	79	80
81	82	83	84	85	86	87	88	89	90
91	92	93	94	95	96	97	98	99	100
101	102	103	104	105	106	107	108	109	110
111	112	113	114	115	116	117	118	119	120
121	122	123	124	125	126	127	128	129	130
131	132	133	134	135	136	137	138	139	140
141	142	143	144	145	146	147	148	149	150
151	152	153	154	155	156	157	158	159	160
161	162	163	164	165	166	167	168	169	170
171	172	173	174	175	176	177	178	179	180
181	182	183	184	185	186	187	188	189	190
191	192	193	194	195	196	197	198	199	200
201	202	203	204	205	206	207	208	209	210
211	212	213	214	215	216	217	218	219	220
221	222	223	224	225	226	227	228	229	230
231	232	233	234	235	236	237	238	239	240
241	242	243	244	245	246	247	248	249	250
251	252	253	254	255	256	257	258	259	260
261	262	263	264	265	266	267	268	269	270
271	272	273	274	275	276	277	278	279	280
281	282	283	284	285	286	287	288	289	290
291	292	293	294	295	296	297	298	299	300

To the Student: Your teacher may ask you to save this chart for use in other activities.

Name Date

Student Sheet 11

Guess My Number Problems

Solve the following problems. If you find only one number that fits, write about how you know it is the only one. If you find more than one number that fits, write about how you know you have found all of the possibilities.

1. My number is less than 50
   My number is a multiple of 6.
   The digits in my number add up to 6.

2. My number is a multiple of 75.
   My number has 3 digits.
   My number is a multiple of 100.

3. My number is less than 100.
   My number is odd.
   My number is a multiple of 7.
   The digits in my number add up to 9.

To the Family

Guess My Number Problems

Session 3

Math Content

Finding multiples
Recognizing relationships among numbers
Using evidence to systematically eliminate possibilities

Materials

Student Sheet 11
300 charts and calculators (optional)

In class, we sometimes spend about ten minutes playing a game called Guess My Number. Students use clues about the characteristics of a mystery number to try to guess the number. For example:

It is less than 50

It is a multiple of 7.

One of its digits is 2 more than the other digit.

For homework, students will solve the Guess My Number problems on Student Sheet 11 and write about their thinking. Does your child think only one number fits the clues, or do several numbers fit? If only one solution exists, how does he or she know it is the only number that fits the clues? If more than one solution is possible, does your child think he or she has them all? How does your child know?

Name Date

Student Sheet 12

34 × 12

Solve this multiplication problem in two ways:

$34 \times 12 =$

Write about how you solved this problem.
Be sure to include:

- what materials you used to solve this problem
- how you solved it
- an explanation of your thinking as you solved it

First Way

Second Way

Name Date

Student Sheet 13

More Multiple Towers

Make a Multiple Tower and answer these questions about the tower you built:

What number did you find the multiples of?

Did your tower include 100 or any multiples of 100 (200, 300, and so on)? Which ones?

If you kept building your tower until it reached the next multiple of 100, how many numbers would be in your tower?

What patterns do you notice in your Multiple Tower?

Name Date

Student Sheet 14

Cluster Problems (page 1 of 2)

Make an estimate for the last problem in each cluster. Then solve the problems in the clusters.

3×50

10×50

34×25

30×50

$\mathbf{34 \times 50}$

Estimate for 34×50 ____________

60×20

62×10

62×3

$\mathbf{62 \times 23}$

Estimate for 62×23 ____________

Name ______________________ Date

Student Sheet 14

Cluster Problems (page 2 of 2)

10×43

30×40

5×43

10×36

$\mathbf{36 \times 43}$

Estimate for 36×43 ____________

10×27

30×20

37×2

40×27

$\mathbf{37 \times 27}$

Estimate for 37×27 ____________

Name Date

Student Sheet 15

Word Problems (page 1 of 3)

JUICE

Cans of juice come in cases of 24.

1. How many cases do you need to open to give one can to each of 250 students?

2. How many cases do you need to open to give one can to each of 500 students?

3. How many cases do you need to open to give one can to each student in your school?

Name Date

Word Problems (page 2 of 3)

CARDS

There are 52 cards in a deck of cards.

1. How many would each person get if the cards were dealt out evenly to 2 people?

2. How many would each person get if the cards were dealt out evenly to 4 people?

3. How many would each person get if the cards were dealt out evenly to 6 people?

4. How many cards would there be in all if 6 students each had a full deck of cards?

Name Date

Student Sheet 15

Word Problems (page 3 of 3)

LUNAR MONTHS

A lunar month—from the day of the new moon to the day of the next new moon—is about 28 days.

1. About how many lunar months are in a year (365 days)?

2. During about how many lunar months are you in school every year?

3. About how many lunar months have gone by since you were born?

Name ________________________________ Date

Student Sheet 16

Division Problems (page 1 of 2)

Make an estimate and then solve each problem. Keep track of your work in such a way that someone looking at it could understand how you solved each problem.

198 ÷ 9 = Estimate ____________

240 ÷ 12 = Estimate ____________

350 ÷ 14 = Estimate ____________

Name Date

Student Sheet 16

Division Problems (page 2 of 2)

Make an estimate and then solve each problem. Keep track of your work in such a way that someone looking at it could understand how you solved each problem.

256 ÷ 16 = Estimate ___________

504 ÷ 24 = Estimate ___________

360 ÷ 11 = Estimate ___________

1	2	3	4	5	6	7	8	9	10
11	12	13	14	15	16	17	18	19	20
21	22	23	24	25	26	27	28	29	30
31	32	33	34	35	36	37	38	39	40
41	42	43	44	45	46	47	48	49	50
51	52	53	54	55	56	57	58	59	60
61	62	63	64	65	66	67	68	69	70
71	72	73	74	75	76	77	78	79	80
81	82	83	84	85	86	87	88	89	90
91	92	93	94	95	96	97	98	99	100
101	102	103	104	105	106	107	108	109	110
111	112	113	114	115	116	117	118	119	120
121	122	123	124	125	126	127	128	129	130
131	132	133	134	135	136	137	138	139	140
141	142	143	144	145	146	147	148	149	150
151	152	153	154	155	156	157	158	159	160
161	162	163	164	165	166	167	168	169	170
171	172	173	174	175	176	177	178	179	180
181	182	183	184	185	186	187	188	189	190
191	192	193	194	195	196	197	198	199	200
201	202	203	204	205	206	207	208	209	210
211	212	213	214	215	216	217	218	219	220
221	222	223	224	225	226	227	228	229	230
231	232	233	234	235	236	237	238	239	240
241	242	243	244	245	246	247	248	249	250
251	252	253	254	255	256	257	258	259	260
261	262	263	264	265	266	267	268	269	270
271	272	273	274	275	276	277	278	279	280
281	282	283	284	285	286	287	288	289	290
291	292	293	294	295	296	297	298	299	300

To the Student: Your teacher may ask you to save this chart for use in other activities.

300 CHART

1	2	3	4	5	6	7	8	9	10
11	12	13	14	15	16	17	18	19	20
21	22	23	24	25	26	27	28	29	30
31	32	33	34	35	36	37	38	39	40
41	42	43	44	45	46	47	48	49	50
51	52	53	54	55	56	57	58	59	60
61	62	63	64	65	66	67	68	69	70
71	72	73	74	75	76	77	78	79	80
81	82	83	84	85	86	87	88	89	90
91	92	93	94	95	96	97	98	99	100
101	102	103	104	105	106	107	108	109	110
111	112	113	114	115	116	117	118	119	120
121	122	123	124	125	126	127	128	129	130
131	132	133	134	135	136	137	138	139	140
141	142	143	144	145	146	147	148	149	150
151	152	153	154	155	156	157	158	159	160
161	162	163	164	165	166	167	168	169	170
171	172	173	174	175	176	177	178	179	180
181	182	183	184	185	186	187	188	189	190
191	192	193	194	195	196	197	198	199	200
201	202	203	204	205	206	207	208	209	210
211	212	213	214	215	216	217	218	219	220
221	222	223	224	225	226	227	228	229	230
231	232	233	234	235	236	237	238	239	240
241	242	243	244	245	246	247	248	249	250
251	252	253	254	255	256	257	258	259	260
261	262	263	264	265	266	267	268	269	270
271	272	273	274	275	276	277	278	279	280
281	282	283	284	285	286	287	288	289	290
291	292	293	294	295	296	297	298	299	300

To the Student: Your teacher may ask you to save this chart for use in other activities.

Name Date

Student Sheet 17

Marvin's Mystery Multiple Tower

This is the top part of Marvin's Multiple Tower.

240
224
208
192
176

What number was Marvin counting by?

How many numbers are in Marvin's tower so far?
How do you know?

If Marvin added 5 more numbers to his tower,
what number would he land on?

What's the next multiple of 100 Marvin would reach?
How did you figure this out?

To the Family

Marvin's Mystery Multiple Tower

Sessions 4–6

Math Content
Finding multiples
Using patterns of multiples of numbers

Materials
Student Sheet 17
Pencil
300 chart, counting materials, and calculators (optional)

In class, we have continued to explore multiplication and division in a variety of ways. To extend our work with Multiple Towers, your child will complete the problems on Student Sheet 17.

1	2	3	4	5	6	7	8	9	10
11	12	13	14	15	16	17	18	19	20
21	22	23	24	25	26	27	28	29	30
31	32	33	34	35	36	37	38	39	40
41	42	43	44	45	46	47	48	49	50
51	52	53	54	55	56	57	58	59	60
61	62	63	64	65	66	67	68	69	70
71	72	73	74	75	76	77	78	79	80
81	82	83	84	85	86	87	88	89	90
91	92	93	94	95	96	97	98	99	100
101	102	103	104	105	106	107	108	109	110
111	112	113	114	115	116	117	118	119	120
121	122	123	124	125	126	127	128	129	130
131	132	133	134	135	136	137	138	139	140
141	142	143	144	145	146	147	148	149	150
151	152	153	154	155	156	157	158	159	160
161	162	163	164	165	166	167	168	169	170
171	172	173	174	175	176	177	178	179	180
181	182	183	184	185	186	187	188	189	190
191	192	193	194	195	196	197	198	199	200
201	202	203	204	205	206	207	208	209	210
211	212	213	214	215	216	217	218	219	220
221	222	223	224	225	226	227	228	229	230
231	232	233	234	235	236	237	238	239	240
241	242	243	244	245	246	247	248	249	250
251	252	253	254	255	256	257	258	259	260
261	262	263	264	265	266	267	268	269	270
271	272	273	274	275	276	277	278	279	280
281	282	283	284	285	286	287	288	289	290
291	292	293	294	295	296	297	298	299	300

To the Student: Your teacher may ask you to save this chart for use in other activities.

Name Date

Student Sheet 18

Finding Factors

Choose a new number. Find the factors of your number using strategies and ideas we talked about in class. Write about the strategies you used and any new patterns you discovered.

My number is ________________.

Its factors are ____.

Strategies I used to find the factors:

____

____

____

____

Patterns I noticed:

____

____

____

____

To the Family

Finding Factors

Sessions 7–8

Math Content
Finding factors
Exploring relationships among factors

Materials
Student Sheet 18
Pencil
300 charts, counting materials, and calculators (optional)

In class, we have been finding factors of large numbers and looking for patterns in the list of factors. For homework, your child will choose two new numbers and find the factors of those numbers. She or he will also look for patterns among the factors. You might suggest that your child think of the number as a quantity of marbles or other objects to be divided evenly. How many people could share the marbles fairly? How many marbles would each person get? Your child may use a 300 chart and counting materials or calculators, if available.

Name Date

Student Sheet 19

How to Play Division Bingo

Materials:

- Completed Multiplication Table: 1 per game for each player
- One deck of Number Cards
- Counters (such as pennies or beans) to cover the numbers

Players: 1 player; a small group; or the whole class

How to Play

1. Take turns drawing a Number Card. Every player then covers one number that is a factor of the card drawn.

2. If a Wild Card is picked, the player who picked it decides on the number to be used. For strategy, the player should choose a number that helps his or her game but does not help the other players.

3. The goal is to cover five numbers in a row—either across, up and down, or diagonally—and get Bingo.

4. Players may choose to continue until the other players also get five in a row.

To the Family

Division Bingo

Session 9

Math Content
Finding factors of large numbers

Materials
Student Sheet 19
Number Cards (to be cut apart into a deck)
Scissors
Envelope or plastic bag for storing a deck of cards (optional)
Several copies of the Completed Multiplication Table
Counters such as pennies or beans (optional)

In class, we have been playing Division Bingo to practice finding factors of large numbers. For homework, your child will play this game with one or more family members. As you play, talk together about the strategies you are using to find factors.

COMPLETED MULTIPLICATION TABLE

	1	2	3	4	5	6	7	8	9	10	11	12
1	1	2	3	4	5	6	7	8	9	10	11	12
2	2	4	6	8	10	12	14	16	18	20	22	24
3	3	6	9	12	15	18	21	24	27	30	33	36
4	4	8	12	16	20	24	28	32	36	40	44	48
5	5	10	15	20	25	30	35	40	45	50	55	60
6	6	12	18	24	30	36	42	48	54	60	66	72
7	7	14	21	28	35	42	49	56	63	70	77	84
8	8	16	24	32	40	48	56	64	72	80	88	96
9	9	18	27	36	45	54	63	72	81	90	99	108
10	10	20	30	40	50	60	70	80	90	100	110	120
11	11	22	33	44	55	66	77	88	99	110	121	132
12	12	24	36	48	60	72	84	96	108	120	132	144

COMPLETED MULTIPLICATION TABLE

	1	2	3	4	5	6	7	8	9	10	11	12
1	1	2	3	4	5	6	7	8	9	10	11	12
2	2	4	6	8	10	12	14	16	18	20	22	24
3	3	6	9	12	15	18	21	24	27	30	33	36
4	4	8	12	16	20	24	28	32	36	40	44	48
5	5	10	15	20	25	30	35	40	45	50	55	60
6	6	12	18	24	30	36	42	48	54	60	66	72
7	7	14	21	28	35	42	49	56	63	70	77	84
8	8	16	24	32	40	48	56	64	72	80	88	96
9	9	18	27	36	45	54	63	72	81	90	99	108
10	10	20	30	40	50	60	70	80	90	100	110	120
11	11	22	33	44	55	66	77	88	99	110	121	132
12	12	24	36	48	60	72	84	96	108	120	132	144

COMPLETED MULTIPLICATION TABLE

	1	2	3	4	5	6	7	8	9	10	11	12
1	1	2	3	4	5	6	7	8	9	10	11	12
2	2	4	6	8	10	12	14	16	18	20	22	24
3	3	6	9	12	15	18	21	24	27	30	33	36
4	4	8	12	16	20	24	28	32	36	40	44	48
5	5	10	15	20	25	30	35	40	45	50	55	60
6	6	12	18	24	30	36	42	48	54	60	66	72
7	7	14	21	28	35	42	49	56	63	70	77	84
8	8	16	24	32	40	48	56	64	72	80	88	96
9	9	18	27	36	45	54	63	72	81	90	99	108
10	10	20	30	40	50	60	70	80	90	100	110	120
11	11	22	33	44	55	66	77	88	99	110	121	132
12	12	24	36	48	60	72	84	96	108	120	132	144

COMPLETED MULTIPLICATION TABLE

	1	2	3	4	5	6	7	8	9	10	11	12
1	1	2	3	4	5	6	7	8	9	10	11	12
2	2	4	6	8	10	12	14	16	18	20	22	24
3	3	6	9	12	15	18	21	24	27	30	33	36
4	4	8	12	16	20	24	28	32	36	40	44	48
5	5	10	15	20	25	30	35	40	45	50	55	60
6	6	12	18	24	30	36	42	48	54	60	66	72
7	7	14	21	28	35	42	49	56	63	70	77	84
8	8	16	24	32	40	48	56	64	72	80	88	96
9	9	18	27	36	45	54	63	72	81	90	99	108
10	10	20	30	40	50	60	70	80	90	100	110	120
11	11	22	33	44	55	66	77	88	99	110	121	132
12	12	24	36	48	60	72	84	96	108	120	132	144

100	180	200	60
98	32	72	150
240	144	324	225
448	396	330	450
Wild Card	Wild Card	Wild Card	Wild Card

	1	2	3	4	5	6	7	8	9	10	11	12
1	1	2	3	4	5	6	7	8	9	10	11	12
2	2	4	6	8	10	12	14	16	18	20	22	24
3	3	6	9	12	15	18	21	24	27	30	33	36
4	4	8	12	16	20	24	28	32	36	40	44	48
5	5	10	15	20	25	30	35	40	45	50	55	60
6	6	12	18	24	30	36	42	48	54	60	66	72
7	7	14	21	28	35	42	49	56	63	70	77	84
8	8	16	24	32	40	48	56	64	72	80	88	96
9	9	18	27	36	45	54	63	72	81	90	99	108
10	10	20	30	40	50	60	70	80	90	100	110	120
11	11	22	33	44	55	66	77	88	99	110	121	132
12	12	24	36	48	60	72	84	96	108	120	132	144

COMPLETED MULTIPLICATION TABLE

	1	2	3	4	5	6	7	8	9	10	11	12
1	1	2	3	4	5	6	7	8	9	10	11	12
2	2	4	6	8	10	12	14	16	18	20	22	24
3	3	6	9	12	15	18	21	24	27	30	33	36
4	4	8	12	16	20	24	28	32	36	40	44	48
5	5	10	15	20	25	30	35	40	45	50	55	60
6	6	12	18	24	30	36	42	48	54	60	66	72
7	7	14	21	28	35	42	49	56	63	70	77	84
8	8	16	24	32	40	48	56	64	72	80	88	96
9	9	18	27	36	45	54	63	72	81	90	99	108
10	10	20	30	40	50	60	70	80	90	100	110	120
11	11	22	33	44	55	66	77	88	99	110	121	132
12	12	24	36	48	60	72	84	96	108	120	132	144

100	180	200	60
98	32	72	150
240	144	324	225
448	396	330	450
Wild Card	Wild Card	Wild Card	Wild Card

Name Date

Student Sheet 20

287 ÷ 14

Think of a situation describing the following problem:

$$287 \div 14 =$$

Write the problem and then solve it.

As you solve the problem, record each step of your work so someone looking at your work would understand your thinking.

COMPLETED MULTIPLICATION TABLE

	1	2	3	4	5	6	7	8	9	10	11	12
1	1	2	3	4	5	6	7	8	9	10	11	12
2	2	4	6	8	10	12	14	16	18	20	22	24
3	3	6	9	12	15	18	21	24	27	30	33	36
4	4	8	12	16	20	24	28	32	36	40	44	48
5	5	10	15	20	25	30	35	40	45	50	55	60
6	6	12	18	24	30	36	42	48	54	60	66	72
7	7	14	21	28	35	42	49	56	63	70	77	84
8	8	16	24	32	40	48	56	64	72	80	88	96
9	9	18	27	36	45	54	63	72	81	90	99	108
10	10	20	30	40	50	60	70	80	90	100	110	120
11	11	22	33	44	55	66	77	88	99	110	121	132
12	12	24	36	48	60	72	84	96	108	120	132	144

	1	2	3	4	5	6	7	8	9	10	11	12
1	1	2	3	4	5	6	7	8	9	10	11	12
2	2	4	6	8	10	12	14	16	18	20	22	24
3	3	6	9	12	15	18	21	24	27	30	33	36
4	4	8	12	16	20	24	28	32	36	40	44	48
5	5	10	15	20	25	30	35	40	45	50	55	60
6	6	12	18	24	30	36	42	48	54	60	66	72
7	7	14	21	28	35	42	49	56	63	70	77	84
8	8	16	24	32	40	48	56	64	72	80	88	96
9	9	18	27	36	45	54	63	72	81	90	99	108
10	10	20	30	40	50	60	70	80	90	100	110	120
11	11	22	33	44	55	66	77	88	99	110	121	132
12	12	24	36	48	60	72	84	96	108	120	132	144

Name Date

How to Play 101 to 200 Bingo

Materials

- 101 to 200 Bingo Board
- One deck of Numeral Cards
- One deck of Tens Cards
- Colored pencil, crayon, or marker

Players: 2 or 3

How to Play

1. Each player takes a 1 from the Numeral Card deck and keeps this card throughout the game.
2. Shuffle the two decks of cards. Place each deck face down on the table.
3. Players use just one Bingo Board. You will take turns and work together to get a Bingo.
4. To determine a play, draw two Numeral Cards and one Tens Card. Arrange the 1 and the two other numerals to make a number between 100 and 199. Then add or subtract the number on your Tens Card. Circle the resulting number on the 101 to 200 Bingo Board.
5. Wild Cards in the Numeral Card deck can be used for any numeral from 0 through 9. Wild Cards in the Tens Card deck can be used as + or – any multiple of 10 from 10 through 70.
6. Some combinations cannot land on the 101 to 200 Bingo Board at all. Make up your own rules about what to do when this happens. (For example, a player could take another turn, or the Tens Card could be *either* added or subtracted in this instance.)
7. The goal is for the players together to circle five adjacent numbers in a row, in a column, or on a diagonal. Five circled numbers is a Bingo.

101 TO 200 BINGO BOARD

101	102	103	104	105	106	107	108	109	110
111	112	113	114	115	116	117	118	119	120
121	122	123	124	125	126	127	128	129	130
131	132	133	134	135	136	137	138	139	140
141	142	143	144	145	146	147	148	149	150
151	152	153	154	155	156	157	158	159	160
161	162	163	164	165	166	167	168	169	170
171	172	173	174	175	176	177	178	179	180
181	182	183	184	185	186	187	188	189	190
191	192	193	194	195	196	197	198	199	200

101 TO 200 BINGO BOARD

101	102	103	104	105	106	107	108	109	110
111	112	113	114	115	116	117	118	119	120
121	122	123	124	125	126	127	128	129	130
131	132	133	134	135	136	137	138	139	140
141	142	143	144	145	146	147	148	149	150
151	152	153	154	155	156	157	158	159	160
161	162	163	164	165	166	167	168	169	170
171	172	173	174	175	176	177	178	179	180
181	182	183	184	185	186	187	188	189	190
191	192	193	194	195	196	197	198	199	200

101	102	103	104	105	106	107	108	109	110
111	112	113	114	115	116	117	118	119	120
121	122	123	124	125	126	127	128	129	130
131	132	133	134	135	136	137	138	139	140
141	142	143	144	145	146	147	148	149	150
151	152	153	154	155	156	157	158	159	160
161	162	163	164	165	166	167	168	169	170
171	172	173	174	175	176	177	178	179	180
181	182	183	184	185	186	187	188	189	190
191	192	193	194	195	196	197	198	199	200

0	0	1	1
0	0	1	1
2	2	3	3
2	2	3	3

4	4	5	5
4	4	5	5
6	6	7	7
6	6	7	7

8	8	9	9
8	8	9	9
WILD CARD	WILD CARD		
WILD CARD	WILD CARD		

TENS CARDS (page 1 of 2)

+10	+10	+10	+10
+20	+20	+20	+20
+30	+30	+30	+40
+40	+50	+50	+60
+70	WILD CARD	WILD CARD	WILD CARD

-10	**-10**	**-10**	**-10**
-20	**-20**	**-20**	**-20**
-30	**-30**	**-30**	**-40**
-40	**-50**	**-50**	**-60**
-70	**WILD CARD**	**WILD CARD**	**WILD CARD**

Name Date

Practice Page A

Solve this problem in two different ways, and write about how you solved it:

$12 \times 4 =$

Here is the first way I solved it:

Here is the second way I solved it:

Name Date

Practice Page B

Solve this problem in two different ways, and write about how you solved it:

63 ÷ 7 =

Here is the first way I solved it:

Here is the second way I solved it:

Name Date

Practice Page C

For each problem, show how you found your solution.

1. Six people gathered 45 oranges from a tree. How many oranges did each one take home?

2. I have 45 oranges. I want to put them in boxes that hold 6 oranges each. How many boxes will I need?

3. I bought 6 oranges. I spent 4 dollars and 50 cents. How much did I spend on each orange?

Name Date

Practice Page D

For each problem, show how you found your solution.

1. Tennis balls come in packages of three. Juan needs 245 balls for an upcoming tournament. How many packages will he have to buy?

2. Ten packages of tennis balls fit in a box. How many boxes will Juan have when he buys the 245 tennis balls he needs?

3. Juan can fit as many as 7 boxes in the trunk of his car. How many will he need to put elsewhere in his car?

300 CHART

1	2	3	4	5	6	7	8	9	10
11	12	13	14	15	16	17	18	19	20
21	22	23	24	25	26	27	28	29	30
31	32	33	34	35	36	37	38	39	40
41	42	43	44	45	46	47	48	49	50
51	52	53	54	55	56	57	58	59	60
61	62	63	64	65	66	67	68	69	70
71	72	73	74	75	76	77	78	79	80
81	82	83	84	85	86	87	88	89	90
91	92	93	94	95	96	97	98	99	100
101	102	103	104	105	106	107	108	109	110
111	112	113	114	115	116	117	118	119	120
121	122	123	124	125	126	127	128	129	130
131	132	133	134	135	136	137	138	139	140
141	142	143	144	145	146	147	148	149	150
151	152	153	154	155	156	157	158	159	160
161	162	163	164	165	166	167	168	169	170
171	172	173	174	175	176	177	178	179	180
181	182	183	184	185	186	187	188	189	190
191	192	193	194	195	196	197	198	199	200
201	202	203	204	205	206	207	208	209	210
211	212	213	214	215	216	217	218	219	220
221	222	223	224	225	226	227	228	229	230
231	232	233	234	235	236	237	238	239	240
241	242	243	244	245	246	247	248	249	250
251	252	253	254	255	256	257	258	259	260
261	262	263	264	265	266	267	268	269	270
271	272	273	274	275	276	277	278	279	280
281	282	283	284	285	286	287	288	289	290
291	292	293	294	295	296	297	298	299	300

To the Student: Your teacher may ask you to save this chart for use in other activities.

Name Date

Practice Page E

Solve each problem. You may want to use a 300 chart to help.

1. Two frogs had a race. Green Frog took 14 jumps of 20. Gray Frog took 8 jumps of 35. Who was ahead? How do you know?

2. In a second race, Green took 6 jumps of 45. Gray took 9 jumps of 30. Who was ahead? How do you know?

3. In the last race, Green decided to take jumps of 50. He took 3 jumps of 50. How many more jumps of 50 did he need to reach 300? How do you know?

Name Date

Practice Page F

Solve each problem. You may want to use a 300 chart to help.

1. Two frogs had a race. Keeper Frog took 2 jumps of 89. Kaller Frog took 3 jumps of 60. Who was ahead? How do you know?

2. In a second race, Keeper took 4 jumps of 55. Kaller took 6 jumps of 36. Who was ahead? How do you know?

3. In the last race, Kaller decided to take jumps of 75. She took 3 jumps of 75. How many more jumps of 75 did she need to reach 300? How do you know?

Practice Page

Solve each problem [illegible]. [illegible] chart to help.

1. Two [illegible] race. [illegible] jumps of 80. Kallie [illegible] jumps of 60. Who was ahead? How do you know?

2. In a second race, [illegible] took 4 jumps of 59. Kallie took 6 jumps of 26. Who was ahead? How do you know?

3. In the last race, Kallie decided to take 6 jumps of 7. [illegible] She took 4 jumps [illegible]. How many more jumps of 7 [illegible]? How do you know?

Name Date

Practice Page G

Solve each problem. You may want to use a 300 chart to help.

1. Two frogs had a race. Lemon Frog took 15 jumps of 8. Lime Frog took 30 jumps of 4. Who was ahead? How do you know?

2. In a second race, Lemon took 8 jumps of 18. Lime took 12 jumps of 12. Who was ahead? How do you know?

3. In the last race, Lime decided to take jumps of 25. She took 7 jumps of 25. How many more jumps of 25 did she need to reach 300? How do you know?